The Life and Rhymes
of Pusscat Grimes

For Lucy, Purdy and Perkins

Published by Keith Abbott Publications 2000

© Keith Abbott and Ben Odbert 2000

ISBN 0-9506553-6-8

Further copies of this book may be obtained from:

Keith Abbott Publications
15 Dunstan Lane
St Mellion
Saltash
England
PL12 6UE

Telephone: 01579-351355
Fax: 01579-351434
E-mail: grimes@abbott2.demon.co.uk

Design and layout Carol Abbott
Printed by PDS Printers, Plymouth

The Life and Rhymes of Pusscat Grimes

by Keith Abbott

Illustrated by Ben Odbert

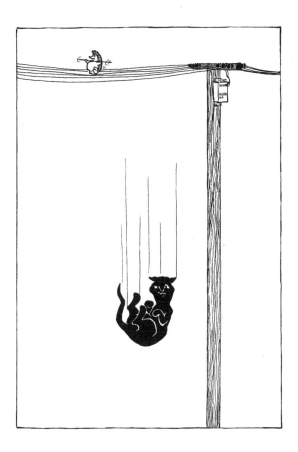

Who is Pusscat Grimes?

Let me introduce myself
My name is Pusscat Grimes
A wicked, but loveable, big black cat
And writer of silly rhymes.

Read about a day in the life of Pusscat Grimes. From
the time he wakes up at 3.50 am until he goes to sleep
at 3.49 am the next day it's all action. Humorous
adventures, poems and cartoons about the wicked, but
loveable Pusscat Grimes and his friends – Toothless
Tom; Boddington, the pub cat; Lumley, his sister;
Douglas, the grumpy magic mouse; Doggo, the dog next
door; and a mystery hedgehog!

Contents

CHAPTER 1

Toilet trouble

Pusscat Grimes fell off the toolbox with a loud thump and a meow. It was 3.50 am, time to go to the toilet and it was dark in the utility room. Despite folklore to the contrary, Pusscat Grimes was living proof that cats can't see in the dark. He missed his litter tray every time on his regular 4.00 am visit, even when he didn't mean to. This time he decided not to use his tray. Lumley had already done something in it. Her tray was un-touched but, as a matter of principle, Pusscat Grimes was not going to use his sister's tray. Why should he use a girl's toilet, especially when it was furthest from his bed?

Pusscat Grimes thought about depositing a pooh behind the central heating boiler, but there was a dried up one still there, undiscovered from last week. So he chose to go on the newspaper next to the tray, pretending that he had missed his tray by mistake. He took his stance. Two legs on the edge of Lumley's tray and two legs on his own, just to show off balancing in the dark. Of course he was just as bad at balancing in the dark as seeing in the dark. Half way through, a front paw slipped. Pusscat Grimes and the tray both went flying, cat litter and pooh spilt everywhere. Pusscat Grimes was rather pleased with the far flung results, so he did a wee on the back door mat as well.

'What a performance,' said Lumley from her position on top of an old computer keyboard. 'You are weak bladdered, your rear end has no sense of direction and you can hardly balance on your own feet, let alone the edge of a litter tray – but it was very entertaining.'

'Hissssss,' said Pusscat Grimes as he licked his bottom. 'I'll sort you out in the morning and tomorrow, for a change, don't eat my breakfast.'

As he dozed off he remembered his first love, Kitty Malone, whom he had fallen for when he was only four months old. Ah, sweet Kitty Malone.

Sweet Kitty Malone

When I was young I resolved to woo
Sweet Kitty Malone, a Russian Blue
She loved her food, or so I'd heard
Anything that moved – toad, goat or bird

'Would you like a dead mouse?'
Was my opening chat-up line
'No I want a live one
I like hot food when I dine'

'Here love try this hedgehog'
Was my next attempt
'I can't eat them they're spiny
And verging on unkempt'

'Let me catch a badger
My love for you to eat'
'Don't be flipping barmy
They're a tasteless cut of meat'

'You're hard to please my sweetpuss
What will make you rave?'
'Get me next door's budgie
It's poultry that I crave'

So I got up on the back of a chair
And stretched my front paws in the air
Then the fowl cried 'Tweet, tweet, tweet'
As I slipped I grabbed with my feet

One got stuck in the bars of its cage
It pecked my paw and got in a rage
Down we went with a meow and squawk
If only my love had settled for pork

I was thrown out for the next three days
And told to mend my wicked ways
I managed to develop a septic paw
It got quite swollen and very sore

Off to the vet I had to go
For an injection in my toe
Next day sweet Kitty sent all her love
Plus one dead budgie and one dead dove

Then she delivered two dead pheasants
I love the girl and her edible presents
It's worth a peck on the end of your toe
To find true love and become a hero.

It was 9.00 am. Pusscat Grimes woke up with a jolt and fell of the toolbox again. It had been an uncomfortable night, but at least the toolbox was now established as his territory. He had been woken up by his owner, Mrs Grimes. She had discovered pooh, wee and litter all over the utility room and was shouting for assistance.

'Harry, Harry Grimes, get down here. He did two last night. I'm sure PG is losing control of his bladder. He is so fat that his stomach is using up all the space where his bladder should be. I'm going to take him to the vet. Harry, Harry are you out of bed? It's your turn to clean it up, I did it yesterday. Harry Grimes – get down here at once.'

'Grimes is off to the vet
Grimes is off to the vet
An injection he will get
In the top of his head
And it will hurt a lot
And grow into a really big spot.'

'Very poetic Lumley, as it happens I like going to the vet. It's always an adventure and an opportunity to reek havoc on a grand scale.'

'More like an opportunity to just reek somewhere else,' said Lumley, as she licked her bottom.

'Yes that too,' said Pusscat Grimes. 'Anyway you remember when I had to go to the vet for all those worming tablets. That proves I like going to the vet.'

A bitter pill

By far the most fun I ever have
Is when they try to give me a pill
It's such a comic performance
That I sometimes pretend to be ill

They get in an absolute frenzy
As they plan their best line of attack
And I love to wind up the tension
By jamming myself in a crack

'Glue it to a Kitti-kat treat
Bury it in the food he'll eat
Get a pea shooter and fire it in
Grab his neck! Hold his chin'

'But I can't get him out
He's stuck in that crack
The one he always goes in
He's gone in head first
For the third time this week
And he's making a dreadful din'

Having got them on the run
I come out to open round two
Before they trap me I'm in my tray
Spending ages doing a pooh

'He's gone in his tray
Is he OK?
He seems to be having a think
Cover the door
Get down on the floor
Head him off at the sink'

Then I allow them to catch me
I pretend to swallow the pill
But I spit it back out in the toaster
By now they are feeling quite ill

I'm off to the vet twelve times this week
To consume one pill each visit
At a cost to old Grimes of £96
Great value I just wouldn't miss it.

CHAPTER 2

A seagull and a magic mouse

Pusscat Grimes was not in his usual good mood. It was 11.00 am. He had overslept and Lumley had eaten his breakfast. Revenge would have to be postponed since she seemed to have disappeared. On the positive side Boddington, the pub cat at the Hairy Dog public house, had a hangover, so he was a little less full of himself than usual. Pusscat Grimes thought Boddington was a good name for a barrel-shaped cat.

The Hairy Dog pub was just across the road from Pusscat Grimes's house. Pusscat Grimes and Boddington had grown up together. Over the years they had had 783 fights, 468 scraps and 253 staring contests, mainly about territory. It was fair to say that their friendship had developed slowly. In the end they agreed that the white line down the middle of the road would divide their territories. Lumley had suggested this after their third fight.

Boddington had quite a reputation locally, partly due to his ability to consume a saucer of strong lager, but mainly because of the legendary seagull incident which Boddington had recounted more times than he'd had live dinners. Pusscat Grimes was one of the few locals old enough to know the truth. The last time Boddington had bored everyone rigid with the story it went something like this.

'Listen you kittens. When I was a lad there was no tinned cat food. Most of us lived on mice, birds and fish heads from the local market. I was the best bird catcher, much quicker than Grimes or Toothless Tom, and I was the toughest, so it was only natural that I used to catch a lot of seagulls. Well there was this one really big one. I'd been hunting it for weeks. He was a clever bird, not one you could just sneak up on and pounce. He seemed to hear me coming even when I did my really low and slow stalking, which I notice so many of you try to copy.

So I hatched a plan to lure the bird to me. Herring would be the bait and I would lie in wait. Hear that Grimes, I can do rhymes. Anyway I sneaked into the fish market and stole a herring. Unseen and unheard I carried it to the harbour, placing it beneath the bird's roost. I waited motionless like a cat, well I would do wouldn't I, but this time I was especially motionless. Only my whiskers moved in the gentle sea breeze.

Eventually something circled overhead. The unsuspecting seagull swooped to take my fishy bait. He was only on the ground for an instant, but an instant was all that Boddington needed. I pounced, we grappled. I'll never forget the look of surprise on his beak as I bit his leg off. He got away, minus one leg. That night I feasted on seagull leg followed by herring, since by good fortune I had bitten off the leg which was grasping the herring.'

Pusscat Grimes told a very different version of the so called 'legend' whenever he had the opportunity.

'Do you remember when Boddington was attacked by a seagull. He was trying to eat a fish head when this seagull decided he fancied fish head for lunch. Boddington was so dozy that he didn't see it coming. When he eventually saw it, he was so scared that his mouth froze shut. The bird grabbed the fish head and Boddington could not let go.

Seagulls are good at flying, but with Boddington on board it could hardly get off the ground. The bird just cleared the first car, but the dangling Boddington did not. He splattered into the windscreen and fell to the ground with a chunk of fish lodged in his mouth. The seagull was so cross that it flew back and pecked Boddington on the nose. This made him meow and drop the last piece of fish. The seagull didn't even bother to fly away. It just ate the piece of fish and waddled into the sunset, leaving Boddington licking his wounds.'

It was nearly midday. Pusscat Grimes and Boddington were in the garden of the Hairy Dog pub.

'Boddington,' said Pusscat Grimes, 'it's nearly opening time and I have not had anything to eat all day. I think I will catch a mouse. Do you want to watch the master mouser at work?'

'I'll bet you one seagull dinner that you will go hungry today, especially as Lumley no doubt ate your breakfast,' said Boddington. 'But I will watch the fun, you may lose an ounce or two of fat.'

Pusscat Grimes and Boddington made their way to the pub garden. Pusscat Grimes practised bottom wiggling and demonstrated his pouncing.

'Mind the nettles Grimes,' chuckled Boddington, as Pusscat Grimes launched himself on his third practice pounce. But it was too late, he landed right in the middle of a patch of stingers.

'Ouch,' came a voice from beneath Pusscat Grimes. 'Get off me you great lump. You are squashing me and suffocating me, and I was already in a bad mood.'

'Hello, hello, hello. What have I landed on? Sounds like a grumpy mouse.' With some difficulty Pusscat Grimes wiggled backwards so that he could get the mouse into his mouth. A moment later he emerged from the nettles, triumphantly carrying the mouse.

'Let me go!' squeaked the mouse. 'You are beginning to make me really cross and you will not like
me when I'm cross. You are dribbling on my fur
and if there is one thing I cannot stand it's cat
dribble in my fur. Oh the embarrassment of being
pounced on by the rear end of an overweight cat.'

'Mouse. Do you taste worse if you are in a bad
mood?' said Boddington hungrily, 'because if you
don't you might as well stop whining and prepare
for dinner.'

'The name is Douglas if you please, Fatty – not
'Mouse'. I am in charge of that nettle patch. It's a
magic nettle patch. I'm a magic mouse and I have
got work to do, so tell Dogbreath to put me down
before I pass out from the smell of kippers.'

'Dogbreath!' barked Pusscat Grimes, realising his
mistake as Douglas Mouse fell to the ground.

'Grimes, you wally wombat. Didn't your mother
teach you not to talk with your mouth full,
especially when you dine out?' said Boddington.

'Rats,' said Pusscat Grimes, as he bent to pick up
Douglas Mouse.

But, as if by magic, Douglas Mouse had disappeared.

Meals on legs

Am I fed up with cat food?
You bet I certainly am
It always tastes exactly the same
Whatever colour the can

It should not be a problem
To give me food I like
Salmon, caviar, trout, prawn
Anchovy, swordfish or pike

Sometimes I go out at night
And have a take away meal
Something with legs, a beak or fur
That if bitten, lets out a squeal

But I pay the price early next day
Because birds are not digestible
They do a U-turn and come straight back up
In the lounge, my bed or the vestibule.

CHAPTER 3

The legendary Toothless Tom

'Not much of a job, being in charge of a patch of nettles. Unless of course they really are magic nettles,' said Pusscat Grimes.

'Well he did disappear once you dropped him, so perhaps he is a magic mouse. More likely you are just short sighted. Talking of poor eyesight, let's visit old Toothless Tom and see if he has recovered from that scrap you had with him.'

Toothless Tom lived in a steel dog kennel in the garden of a house a few doors away from Pusscat Grimes. When he was young he was the toughest cat in the street, undefeated in 1382 fights over a 15-year period. To maintain his tough reputation, Tom would sometimes sleep in the middle of the road. Some people, put this down to poor eyesight and hearing. Passers-by used to carry him back to the pavement. Tom also boasted about his ability to eat slugs. Pusscat Grimes thought this was something to do with his toothlessness. Toothless Tom still loved to fight and all the local cats would take turns to scrap with him.

Toothless Tom

I got in a fight the night before last
With Toothless Tom a foe from the past
He lives at number twenty-three
Which is roughly his age, or so he told me

But despite his ever advancing years
He absolutely has no fears
He'll pick a scrap with anyone
He doesn't need a reason, he fights for fun

Once he gets started he's completely nuts
He'll bite your ears and scratch your guts
But when I say 'bite' it's not really true
He doesn't have teeth so he can't hurt you

And by the way he's lost his claws
So the bottom of his legs just end in paws
So when I say 'scratch' it's more like a stroke
It doesn't hurt at all, it's a bit of a joke

But Toothless Tom makes a fearful noise
By far the loudest of all the boys
But due to fate, an unkind quirk
He can't hear a thing since his ears don't work

So he rushes into battle with an off key 'meow'
He'll tackle a dog, a postman or cow
From his point of view they're all the same
His object is to kill or at least to maim

Whatever their size he doesn't seem to mind
Maybe it's because he's almost blind
So his foes emerge totally unscathed
Somewhat puzzled, but not enraged

But this doesn't mean Tom can't do harm
Since after each battle he turns on the charm
And engages all present in endless prattle
Of vanquished postman, dogs and cattle

He'll talk and talk till his very last breath
If you don't escape he'll bore you to death.

'You know Grimes,' said Boddington, 'the reason Tom got started with all this fighting was to defend his name. Not all cats have sensible names like 'Grimes' and 'Boddington'. Pedigree cats have silly names and although Tom is a moggy like the rest of us, his daft owners gave him a silly name. When you combine a silly name with almost no brain and a total disregard for personal safety, you get one very mean fighting cat.'

'And of course,' said Pusscat Grimes, 'it's a real disadvantage when it comes to romance. Tom has only had about 2300 girlfriends over the years, whereas you and I must have had ten times that amount.'

What's in a name?

In my house they have sensible names
Like Margaret, Lucy and Frederick
Even the gerbils sound quite sane
If you're impressed by Cecil and Cedric

Boddington's mates have been christened
With names of which they are proud
There's Barney, Buster, Felix, Fred
Kojak, Columbo and McCloud

But when Tom goes to the market
To try to chat up a bird
It's a terrible disadvantage
Being 'Thomas Fishcake the Third'.

When they arrived at Tom's house he was trying to wash his bottom. All cats find this rather difficult. It puts a strain on the lower back. Of course if you are 23 it's almost impossible. The best Tom could do was to lick half way down his tail.

'Hello Tom,' said Boddington, before he remembered that Tom was so deaf that a more traditional greeting would be needed to announce their arrival.

'Your turn I think,' said Boddington to Pusscat Grimes. Very reluctantly Pusscat Grimes approached Tom and sniffed his bottom. Feeling like he was going to be sick, he turned round so that Tom could sniff his bottom.

'Aah lovely,' croaked old Tom. 'I'd recognise that smell anywhere. Hello, Lumley, my dear. Have you come to hear the story of one of my battles? I'm sure you have you pretty thing. Well, you will not be disappointed. Only yesterday I vanquished that overweight brother of yours. Came at me from behind he did, waving his paws and squealing like a piglet. I dodged to the left. He tripped over my tail and banged his head on my kennel. I fixed him with my fiercest stare and... ZZZZZ.'

'That's a new trick' said Boddington 'falling asleep in the middle of a sentence. He must be beginning to bore himself to death. Shall I wake him up?'

'Only if you want my paw scratching your beak,' said Pusscat Grimes.

'When did you last wash your bottom, Grimes' said Boddington. 'I am amazed that he did not recognise you.'

'Listen, Boddington, bottom washing is obviously unhealthy so I have decided to give it up.'

'Impossible,' said Boddington. 'I hate washing mine, but it's programmed into us. If you don't do it, your brain turns to custard. You wait and see. It goes yellow and comes out of your ears. Bother, all this talk of bottoms has made me want to wash mine now.'

Mother nature

I get a terrible back ache
As I sit with one leg in the air
I've got a nasty taste in my mouth
And as usual a few bits of hair

Instinct is a cruel mistress
To force me to act in this way
And lick my own posterior
At least six times each day.

'You know Boddington,' said Pusscat Grimes, 'that Toothless Tom has always been a slave to instinct, especially his climbing instinct. A strong climbing instinct, combined with madness and a total disregard for personal safety produces some pretty lively situations.'

'Electrifying and shocking, I would say,' said Boddington. 'He must have climbed at least a hundred telegraph poles. I know that he has been electrocuted more than 20 times. It's fortunate that now that he has lost his claws he can only get about half way up before he slithers down. Grimes, you used to have the fire brigade out every week when you were younger due to your inability to climb down from anything.'

The only way is up

I really cannot help myself
I have this urge to climb
I love to zoom up telegraph poles
I choose them every time

I'm jolly good at going up
It's daring and it's fun
I'm not so good at coming down
So far I've climbed down none.

CHAPTER 4

Doggo's rubber bone

Pusscat Grimes's brain was beginning to recover from a rather custardy feeling. Instinct had defeated him and he had washed his bottom three times in the last hour. He needed a good laugh to cheer him up and there was nothing better than visiting Doggo, the dog next door.

Pusscat Grimes liked to spy on Doggo from the roof of the garden shed. As usual Doggo was in the garden. For the last three days he had been digging holes all over the garden. Doggo was frantic. His little paws were sore from non-stop digging. The last person he wanted to see was Pusscat Grimes.

'Grimes,' said Doggo, 'you are the last animal I want to see unless you know where Lumley buried my favourite rubber bone.'

'Is that the reason for all this digging? Well you're not digging deep enough holes. I'm sure that she will have buried it much deeper than that. I may be wrong, but it could be in the rose bed.'

In fact, it was in Lumley's bed. She seemed to like the smell of rubber, so she had slept with the bone for the last three nights. Not very healthy, sleeping with a rubber bone, thought Pusscat Grimes, so he resolved to return it to Doggo – by air mail.

A few minutes later Pusscat Grimes was back in Doggo's garden. In complete silence, bone in mouth, he climbed the large conker tree which towered over the rose bed. He had a perfect view of Doggo's rear end (which was nowhere near as clean as his own) as it disappeared into a rather large hole for a small dog. Taking careful aim Pusscat Grimes lobbed the bone out of the tree. There was a startled yelp as it hit is target. Poor little Doggo could hardly climb out of the hole it was so deep. When he did get out he was so confused that he did not know whether to bark, chew his bone, or dig another hole and bury it himself. In the end he settled for barking.

My pet hate

My pet hate is the pet next door
A little chap of one foot four

He cannot take a joke you see
A problem if you live near me

There was the time I took his bone
He woofed and yelped and had a moan

He thought it was buried underground
So he dug 50 holes, deep and round

But he doesn't know psychology
Cat plus bone equals top of tree

And he doesn't have a sense of humour
Lucky for him I'm not a puma!

You know the rest, bone fell to ground
With great precision, it hit the hound

'Good shot old chap,' he should have said
Instead he woofed, till he went to bed.

CHAPTER 5

The art of path crossing

It was 5.00 pm. Pusscat Grimes and Boddington were back at their favourite meeting place in the garden of the Hairy Dog pub.

'Boddington, do you believe in reincarnation?' said Pusscat Grimes.

'Of course not, you silly old fool. I don't believe in it now and I didn't when I was a frog.'

'Yes, very funny, but you are superstitious aren't you? After all you carried a rabbit's foot around for two weeks last summer, or was that just to prove that you actually caught a rabbit? And we know that cats have nine lives.'

'Except if you get run over by a combine harvester,' said Boddington, 'as proved by poor Kojak last August, God rest his soul. All nine lives gone at once. You have got no chance when the grim reaper starts using modern technology.'

Nine lives

I've heard there is a theory
That a cat dropped from a height
Will twist to land on all four feet
At some point in its flight

Me, I have an enquiring mind
I'll test scientific laws
I'll jump from a top floor window
And try to land on my paws

Will I land the wrong way up
And possibly slip a disk?
Will I use a precious life?
What is the degree of risk?

In the end I got the worst of both worlds
My life it did me fail
I twisted to land the right way up
But missed and sprained my tail.

'Anyway,' said Pusscat Grimes, 'I don't really mind if I don't have nine lives, because I'm black, and black is the luckiest colour for a cat and the only colour which gives the magical power to dish out bad luck.'

Tit-for-tat cat

A black cat crossed my path today
It said 'Take that' and ran away

The silly mammal had some pluck
To try to end my run of luck

You see my coat is also black
So I caught him up and crossed him back.

Pusscat Grimes and Boddington were in the bar, practising hissing, when there was a dull thump behind them, followed by a squeaky 'Bother'.

'Look what has just appeared from nowhere. It's a magic mouse,' said Pusscat Grimes.

'That was not magic, I just fell off the ceiling,' squeaked Douglas. 'I was chewing through the lighting wires because lights keep me awake at night, so don't distract me by making silly noises. Walking on the ceiling is difficult enough without a couple of old moggies putting me off.'

'Will it put you off if we eat you?' said Boddington.

'Don't put me in an even worse mood than before, or else you really will be in big trouble. I'll turn you into a lizard, with my new lizard spell.' Douglas swayed as he began to chant.

'Foot of mouse and tail of rat
Prepare to transmoggify one fat cat
In three simple steps that never fail
Starting with whiskers, ending with tail.'

'Hocus pocus,' said the mousy wizard,
'Turn this cat into a lizard
To complete this spell, there's one last word
Which I've forgotten – how absurd!'

'I don't suppose it's 'abracadabra',' said Pusscat Grimes. 'I mean if I can assist with Boddington's transmoggification, I would only be too pleased to help.' Pusscat Grimes turned to see if Boddington was cat or lizard and was rather upset to see two stone of sleeping cat. He turned back to the mouse. But, as if by magic, Douglas Mouse had disappeared.

'Wake up, Boddington. You obviously neutered his spell by sleeping through it and the mouse has mysteriously vanished again. Now back to the serious business of administering bad luck. As you know the milkman doesn't like cats and I don't like milkmen. I especially don't like our milkman. I'm sure he trod on my paw on purpose. So I've been practising. Watch and learn.'

For the next 10 minutes Pusscat Grimes was almost motionless, except for mysterious backward movements of one hind leg.

'Excuse me asking,' said Boddington, 'but what am I supposed to be learning, how to stand on three legs looking like a complete wombat?'

'Ssshhh, you broke my concentration. I almost had it. If I can walk backwards it will double my potency. With about 16 stone of milkman on the receiving end, I need all my bad luck powers.'

'Waste of time,' chuckled Boddington. 'Cats can't walk backwards, we can't even walk sideways. It's ten forward gears, nothing in reverse. Probably something to do with our knees. You know all this. You even wrote a poem about it, just after you spent three weeks in that new cattery, the one with all that piped rap music.'

Best foot backwards

Some black cats will walk forwards as they try to
cross your path
A few will shuffle sideways as they try to get a
laugh
One or two will try to cross you by falling from a
tree
But none of these are up to scratch for the master
– yes that's me

When I want to cast a real good curse
I don't walk forwards, I proceed in reverse

About 10 steps are all you need
To complete your wicked catty deed

You can walk tall or crouch very low
As seeds of bad luck you gleefully sow

Get your fur standing all on end
Arch that back, let's see it bend

Throw your tail up, high in the air
Go meow meow, like you just don't care

Get off the wall, get down on the floor
Meow meow again, move your left back paw

Opposite front is your next cool move
Just three inches back, get in the groove

Shift your back right, smooth and easy
Waggle that tail like it's easy peasy

One more corner to get into gear
Move leg number four, show no fear

Now all four legs, let's do it again
Two, four, six, seven, eight, nine, ten

Come on you cats it's mind over matter
Let's hear those paws make a backwards patter

When you've finished this wicked rap
Go meow meow again and take a nap

Yeah

So the forward walking cats deal out small doses
of bad luck
The sideways ones get laughed at, but they show a
lot of pluck
The ones that fall from trees are really not that
bright
So put your best foot backwards each and every
night.

'You can practise all you like, but I tell you it's impossible,' said Boddington. 'If we were supposed to walk backwards our fur would point in the opposite direction and we would have eyes in our bottoms. I'm off for dinner. Bye.'

CHAPTER 6

Havoc at the vet

Pusscat Grimes arrived home just in time to see Lumley sitting by his empty plate and licking her lips. She carefully groomed her face with her paw and strode off towards the lounge. Pusscat Grimes made a mental note to sort her out later.

'PG,' said Mrs Grimes, 'where have you been all day? You have an appointment with the vet at 6.30, about being too fat. You knew that and you still stayed out far too late.'

Pusscat Grimes surveyed the kitchen from his vantage point on top of the cooker hood and thought about what Mrs Grimes had said.

'I'm a cat, so I'm not supposed to understand the English language and I don't wear a watch. My coming and going is governed by animal instinct, in this case the need for tinned cat food. And what do I find – an empty plate, my smug sister licking her lips and the cat basket in the middle of the floor. Well let's see if you can get me down from here.'

Mrs Grimes was already on a chair and had Pusscat Grimes by the front legs. Battle commenced. Pusscat Grimes squeezed himself back against the wall and braced his back legs against the front of the cooker hood. Pusscat Grimes and his owner both bared their teeth and snarled. Their eyes met as they tugged in opposite directions. The deadlock was eventually broken when the cooker hood detached itself from the wall and they both crashed to the floor. Mrs Grimes screamed, but rather than break her fall, she kept both hands clamped on Pusscat Grimes. Before he had recovered she managed to get him in the basket and shut the lid. Mrs Grimes was still muttering as she carried Pusscat Grimes to the car.

'You stupid cat. Do you want to be fat for the rest of you life, which may only be a few hours if you give me any more trouble? Do you enjoy having no control over your bladder? Don't you realise that you are going to the vet for your own good? Who is going to pay for a new cooker hood?'

'Yes', 'yes', 'you must be joking' and 'not me' thought Pusscat Grimes in answer to the four questions. What a nuisance it is that only other animals understand me.

If I could talk

As a highly intelligent mammal
I know what I want to say
I know when I want to say it
And how many times a day

'I want my food
Let me out know
Open the flipping door
Get off my chair
Turn on the fire
Ouch, you trod on my paw'

I've practised long and loud
I've even tried saying 'bow wow'
But to my eternal frustration
It always comes out as 'meow'.

It was only a three-minute drive to the vet, but Pusscat Grimes managed to empty half his bladder in his cat basket during the journey. He really enjoyed his regular visits to the vet. This time it was really amusing to hear Mrs Grimes explaining her theory about his stomach taking up bladder space and causing lack of control. Right on time, just as the vet was feeling his tummy, Pusscat Grimes went to the toilet again, emptying the half of his bladder that he had saved from the journey.

Fresh, warm, slippery cat wee trickled off the table and on to the vet's floor. At just that moment a veterinary nurse came in from the resuscitation room carrying a little cage containing a sick little gerbil who was recovering from an operation to fix her dislocated tail.

'Careful of the slippery...' but it was too late. Nurse and gerbil both went base over apex. Obeying the laws of gravity, they both landed at the same time, making rather similar squeaking noises. It turned out that they had similar injuries. The gerbil dislocated its tail again and the nurse dislocated her elbow.

In the confusion Pusscat Grimes escaped into the waiting room, and spent five minutes wailing and hissing before he was finally back in his cat basket, but not without the usual struggle. All in all it was one of his more enjoyable visits to the vet.

CHAPTER 7

Furballs and catflaps

Pusscat Grimes knew that there was nothing wrong with him and he was not surprised when the vet diagnosed that Mrs Grimes had probably been over-feeding him. This set her off again.

'Stupid vet blaming me for your fatness. Two wees in ten minutes. Why do you do it? Next time you go on the cooker hood I'll turn the gas on and then we'll see how long you stay up there. You are probably so stupid that you would catch fire before you even thought about coming down. And why are you sitting by your plate? Do you really think that I'm going to feed you? I think you should not eat for at least three days. Now stop that meowing and rubbing on my leg Grimes dear. All right, just half a tin of pilchards and a portion of cooked duck breast. There's a good boy.'

Pusscat Grimes ate all of the food, because he was hungry and to make sure that Lumley could not eat it. Then he decided to have a short nap, since he had noticed that he had clean bedding. He had been training Mrs Grimes to wash his bedding every week.

Sweet smelling dreams

Some cats sleep in the same place
But routine isn't for me
I can't stand catty bedding
It could easily give me a flea

Give me a freshly washed jumper
Or a clean white pillow case
Anything that has just been bought
Or that's made of silk and lace

When you get it back again
It will have a rich pussy smell
I'll leave a bit of my fur on it
And maybe a toe-nail as well.

Pusscat Grimes had only tested his clean bedding for about ten minutes. He was in the lounge and he was planning. To an observer it looked like sleeping, but planning it was. As the body rested, the mind worked overtime. How would he get revenge on the milkman? But first he needed to sort out a rather troublesome furball that was just beginning to cause a tickle in his stomach.

A furry friend

On a cold winter's night to my owner's delight
I curl up in front of the fire
I've just had my tea and I'm sweet as could be
Everything you could desire

I have a short nap then jump on your lap
You stroke me and I start to purr
But you don't know me it's a cover you see
As I quietly regurgitate fur

I jump to the ground and let out a sound
Like a llama trying to be sick
'Why can't he go out the silly trout
He must be incredibly thick'

Well thick I'm not, but I do feel too hot
I'm a warm-blooded furry mammal
So I hit the deck, extend my neck
And make a noise like a strangled camel

All this time, throughout this rhyme
The furball's been under my tongue
So with it still there I get on a chair
To see where it can be flung

For a minute or two there's nothing to do
As they take some anti-stress drug
As they start to unwind to their horror they find
That it's just popped out on the rug.

Grimes surveyed the furball with pride. It was a really good one, mainly fur, but some grass and pilchard.

'PG, you stupid stupid stupid cat, all over my new rug. If only you could have managed it six inches to the left and you would had done it on *The Sunday Times* instead of my rug. You are going out. I don't care if it is cold and that the stupid vet upset both of us. Harry, Harry Grimes, where are you? He's vomited in the lounge, clear it up, quickly before it soaks into my new rug. I'm putting him out Harry, Harry!'

The next instant strong hands grabbed Pusscat Grimes and he was in the air, held at arm's length by the angry Mrs Grimes. As luck would have it, the back door had been locked and the key was not in the lock. Now cat flaps are designed to be operated by a cat without the assistance of a human, but this was not going to put off a determined Mrs Grimes. Her first attempt to force him through forwards was hopeless. Pusscat Grimes did a sort of starfish or octopus impression with all four legs that made him at least twice the size of the cat flap. After a short struggle all Mrs Grimes had to show for her efforts were scratches on the paintwork on the back of the door.

For her next attempt Pusscat Grimes was swivelled round and forced through backwards. This time the entire cat actually went through the cat flap as a result of a firm push by Mrs Grimes in Pusscat Grimes's stomach, but Mrs Grimes's arm also went through the cat flap and embedded in the sleeve of her jumper were the 16 claws on Pusscat Grimes's four feet. However hard she shook she could not dislodge him. She briefly considered trying to take off her jumper and stuff it through the flap, but common sense prevailed as she withdrew her arm, together with its furry attachment, back into the kitchen.

One by one Mrs Grimes detached the embedded claws from her jumper. One by one Pusscat Grimes re-attached them. 'Harry, where are you? When you have cleared up the mess, chuck PG out. Harry Grimes, Harry have you gone down the pub? Harry.' Mrs Grimes slumped to the floor.

Pusscat Grimes had milkman business to attend to so he detached himself from Mrs Grimes's jumper, strolled over to his flap and disappeared through it. A moment later Lumley came in the same way carrying a live mouse. As the cat flap closed Pusscat Grimes caught a glimpse of Mrs Grimes on her hands and knees firmly hanging on to one of Lumley's back legs.

Cat flaps

Who invented the cat flap?
I'll scratch him with my paw
I much prefer the personal touch
When a human opens the door.

CHAPTER 8

More toilet trouble and more magic mouse

Pusscat Grimes and Boddington were back in the garden of the Hairy Dog. Boddington was in a rather silly mood. He had eaten one and a half tins of kipper flavoured catfood, washed down with a saucer of brown ale. He was desperate to go to the toilet, but instinct had delayed proceedings and he was digging the obligatory hole. Mud and stones flew everywhere as he scrabbled frantically at the surface of a flower bed. Unfortunately, in older cats bladder control usually triumphs over instinct and just before the hole was finished, Boddington relieved himself on the path.

'Bother, that wasn't supposed to happen,' said Boddington. 'Grimes I've done it on the path. What do I do now – fill in the hole or shovel some mud on to the path? I can't remember.'

'Can't you move the wet dirt from the path into the hole?' chuckled Pusscat Grimes.

'Don't be stupid. Firstly, I would get wee on my paws and secondly the wee would not be properly buried. Instinct doesn't seem to cover toilet accidents.'

'All right, leave it where it is until nature evolves the answer for us.' said Pusscat Grimes. Boddington agreed but he still could not resist filling in a little of the hole as he walked past.

'It may be dark,' said Boddington as he stumbled into a dustbin, 'but I'm going to catch that magic mouse. It's obvious that if I eat a magic mouse my own magic powers will increase.'

'You don't think it is a problem that you can't see in the dark and that your sense of smell is numbed by all that kipper flavoured cat food?'

Night sight

Can I catch a mouse in the local park?
What do you think when it's totally dark?

They're tricky to catch in the full light of day
If you try it at night they get away

It's just not true about pussy cat sight
We can't see a thing in twilight or night.

'What is that awful smell? It smells like rotting fish and overweight cat,' said a rather squeaky voice. 'I just trod in something very unpleasant on the path and it's put me in a really really bad mood, so if one of you would own up I'll turn you into a woodlice and be on my way.'

'It was me,' said Boddington, 'and you have fallen into my trap. Just as soon as this smell of kippers is out of my system I'll be able to track you down from the smell of your feet, and then we'll dine together, with you as the main course. Where are you? I can hear you, but I can't see you.'

'Of course you can't see me,' said Douglas, 'I'm cloaked with invisibility, whereas you are so fat you are blocking out all the moonlight. The sooner you are reduced to the size of a woodlice the better. This time don't fall asleep during the spell.' Douglas swayed invisibly as he began to chant.

'Foot of mouse and tail of rat
Prepare to transmoggify one fat cat
Three simple steps will confirm your fears
Starting with tail, ending with ears.'

'Abracadabra' said the magic mouse
'Turn this cat into a louse
To complete the spell, there's one last word
Which I've forgotten...'

'What a nerd.' said Pusscat Grimes in an attempt to complete the spell. He turned to see if Boddington had turned into a woodlice. 'You look like a cat, but it's the inner person that matters. Do you feel like a woodlice?'

'Grimes, stop talking drivel. Where is that mouse? I'm hungry.'

But, as if by magic, Douglas Mouse had disappeared.

CHAPTER 9

Revenge on Udder's dairy

'Here's the plan,' whispered Pusscat Grimes to Boddington, as they crouched beneath the hedge outside Udder's Dairy. 'You stay out here. You are the getaway cat, so don't fall asleep. I will squeeze through the tiny gap in the fence. I'll cross the yard in a flash, dodging the searchlights. Then I will walk along the top of the wooden fence on the far side of the yard.'

'Instinct or showing off?' said Boddington.

'Quiet,' hissed Pusscat Grimes, 'I'll jump from the fence into the bottling plant and have a drink of milk. Then I'll be back on top of the fence.'

'Showing off,' said Boddington.

'I'll be back on the fence so that I can jump silently into the dirty puddle near to where the milk floats are loaded. Before you can say 'go for it Grimes' I'll have muddied all four paws. Crouching so low as to be almost invisible, I will sneak up on the unsuspecting milk float. Two minutes later the deed will be done. Precisely 42 seconds later, I'll be back out here.'

'And jump into the getaway cat I suppose,' said the getaway cat.

'No, you are a decoy getaway cat. You run off down Catkin Avenue. I'll scarper down Ferkin Terrace. There probably won't be any pursuers, but if there are they will be confused and I'll be away clean.'

'Except for your feet,' said Boddington with a chuckle. 'You'll be a rebel without clean paws!'

'And we will rendevous at 2230 hundred hours back at the pub,' said Pusscat Grimes.

'We'll do what and when?' said a puzzled Boddington, but Pusscat Grimes was already up through the fence and into the yard.

The mark of the dirty paw

Last Tuesday, just three days ago
The milkman purposely squashed my toe
Since then it's been my one ambition
To execute a fearless mission
To deposit the mark of the dirty paw
On bonnet, roof, seat and door

The deed was done in the dead of night
Next day my foe got such a fright
As a result of daring and feline cunning
The effect I achieved was totally stunning
Three hundred black paw prints on his milk float
Ah sweet revenge, now it's my turn to gloat.

Remarkably the mission was successful, well reasonably successful. Pusscat Grimes did fall off the fence eight times, and the whole exercise took about 10 minutes, but no one saw Pusscat Grimes and the milk float was suitably muddied. When he returned, Boddington was asleep, so Pusscat Grimes pounced on his tail to celebrate his success. Boddington awoke with a jolt. He immediately remembered his duty as the getaway cat and shot off down Catkin Avenue as fast as his little legs would carry him. Pusscat Grimes stood and watched with interest.

'It's already turned to custard,' he muttered.

CHAPTER 10

Boddington's transmoggification

'Boddington,' said Pusscat Grimes, 'your valuable contribution as getaway cat ensured the success of the mission. It also amused me and lost you another ounce of fat. Later tonight I shall present you with a magic mouse as your reward.'

'Save it Grimes, I'm too knackered even to talk to that mouse, let alone eat it. Anyway, all that running has bluntened my claws. I need my scratching post.'

Boddington's scratching post was in fact the garden gate, so he only had a few yards to go. He breathed a sigh of relief as he sunk his claws into the rough wood and began to claw vigorously.

'You realise that all that clawing just makes them blunter,' said Pusscat Grimes.

'So why do you do yours, PG?' said a voice from the top of the fence. 'Regular as clockwork, every night at 3.00 am – a slave to instinct you are, PG. I know that you think I'm asleep, but I'm not. I see you using that silly scratching post with a plastic ball that they bought from the petshop. Not like

Boddington who, like a real man, deliberately gives himself splinters every night.'

Boddington winced and looked at his paws, but it was too dark to see anything.

'Thank you very much Lumley,' said Pusscat Grimes. 'As it happens the only reason I scratch my post at 3.00 am every night is to wake you up. Instinct does not govern Pusscat Grimes.'

'Except the instinct to lick your bottom,' Boddington reminded him.

'PG,' said Lumley very smugly, 'you can't wake me up if I am not asleep.'

Catnaps

The cat nap is a total myth
Me, I never sleep
I know that I can fool you
And every three seconds I peep.

'Anyway, the night is young,' said Pusscat Grimes.

'And we're young and full of kippers,' said Boddington, to strange looks from the others.

'And the world is your rooster,' said Lumley.

'Shut up the lot of you,' said a rather squeaky voice. 'My magic powers don't work so well if I'm tired because stupid cats have kept me awake all night!'

'Lumley,' said Boddington, 'let me introduce Douglas Mouse, edible owner of a patch of stinging nettles, victim of Grimes's famous rear end pounce, forgetter of magic words, chewer of electric cables, treader in of things he would rather not have trodden in, and generally the grumpiest magic mouse that lives in the garden of the Hairy Dog public house. Have you any last requests mouse, before I gobble you up?'

'Yes, as I already said you cloth-eared, overweight, mangy moggy, just shut up or I will turn you into a flea with my new flea spell. In fact, I'm going to turn you into a flea even if you don't shut up, so shut up a prepare to become a flea.' Douglas swayed as he began to chant.

'Foot of mouse and tail of rat
Please please transmoggify this fat cat
Three simple steps short and sweet
Starting with head, ending with feet'

'Alakazan' said the mouse of mystery
'Turn this cat from cat to cat flea
To complete this spell, there's one last word
Which I've forgotten...'

'... So we heard... or not as the case seems to be,'
said Lumley, 'but don't despair magic mouse. I can
see a flea on this fat cat's ear. Perhaps the flea is
Boddington and the fat cat is a transmoggified
flea. Yes, I think the spell has worked. The cat is
clearly on the flea, not the flea on the cat. Let us
grieve for the departed Boddington and welcome
into our midst this new friend, formerly a flea, who
seems to bear some resemblance to our late mate
Boddington.'

'You are as daft as your daft brother. When you are quite finished talking complete drivel,' said Boddington, 'I have a mouse to consume.'

But, as if by magic, Douglas Mouse had disappeared.

'PG,' said Lumley, 'do you remember when you had an infestation of fleas? Always scratching you were and they laid flea eggs in you bed and you whined all the time and you had to be flea sprayed every day and you even had to wear a flea collar. How absolutely embarrassing for you and great fun for the rest of us. It even used to give you bad dreams didn't it. Do you remember the one about the giant fleas on the planet Rat?'

The planet Rat

I had a weird dream the other night
I'd been fired into outer space
I landed on a planet called 'Rat'
A remote and spooky place

'Take me to your leader,'
I said to a giant flea
The flea said 'No, you'd better go
You're far too clever for me.'

'I know that I fly a spaceship
But that doesn't mean I'm clever,'
'Too blooming true,' the giant flea said
'Since you can't leave here, not ever.'

'You see my boy' it went on to say
'The gravity here is so strong
You can't go up a single inch
Only sideways, down or along.'

'Only us fleas with our powerful legs
Can make any upward progress
Everyone else is stuck on the ground
And us fleas, we just couldn't care less.'

I was scared as a scardy cat
My knees were starting to buckle
I was jolly glad when I woke up
So I had a little chuckle.

'Come on,' said Pusscat Grimes. 'It's getting late and we have people to keep awake. Let's go and get Toothless Tom. The three cats set off for Tom's house. Every few steps Boddington launched himself a few inches into the air, just to try to convince Lumley that he really was a flea. Lumley held her head high in the air and ignored him.

CHAPTER 11

Scrapping and singing

They arrived at Toothless Tom's house on the stroke of midnight. Toothless Tom was asleep outside his old steel dog kennel. The three cats sniffed at old Tom, Pusscat Grimes prodded him with a paw, Lumley stood on his tail. Eventually Boddington found just enough ear to get his teeth into and took a firm hold.

The effect was dramatic. Toothless Tom woke instantly and sprang three feet into the air hissing and wailing. A startled Boddington let go of his ear. Tom twisted in the air and skilfully landed on Boddington's back facing the tail end. He landed mouth first and sunk his gums into that part of a cat that doesn't have a name, just where the tail joins the rest of the cat. Boddington jumped up and down and spun round like a whirling dervish, but Toothless Tom held fast.

'He fights like a flea,' said Lumley, 'all that jumping up and down and whining.'

Eventually Boddington managed to jump and twist at the same time so that he landed flat on his back, with Toothless Tom beneath him. Two stone of pub cat was too much for Toothless Tom and he eventually let go.

'Let that be a lesson to you Boddington. Yes, I know it's you, as soon as I sunk my gums into your bottom I recognised your distinctive aroma. Your identity was confirmed by your pathetic attempts to do battle and your excessive weight falling on top of me. I suppose you brought Grimes with you. I was going to find my kennel. Someone stole it last night, but no doubt you want me to lead you in a chorus of catawauling and singing. Come on then, follow me and stay close.'

Toothless Tom turned around and strode proudly off… straight into his kennel. There was a metallic clunk as his head hit the rear wall. A few seconds later Tom strode proudly out of his kennel.

The four cats balanced precariously on Doggo's fence. Boddington kept one set of claws in Pusscat Grimes to help him balance and they began to sing.

The cool cat rock

There's one old song we cats love to sing
Every morning at one o'clock
It's really loud and it's just our thing
It's called the Cool Cat Rock

'C'mon let's wail again, like we did last summer
Yeah, let's wail again, like we did last year
C'mon let's howl some more, so your throat gets
nummer
Yeah, let's squeal again, like Tom's got your ear

Round and round and up and down we wail again
Wake up, don't sleep, get down and twist that tail
again

C'mon let's wail again, like we did last summer
Yeah, let's wail again, like we did last night
C'mon let's make more noise, like a real loud
drummer
Yeah, let's howl again, like it's a real prize fight

Round and round and up and down we wail again
With a noise like this we're never gonna fail again

C'mon let's wail again like we did last summer
Yeah, let's wail again, like we did last week
C'mon let's shout out loud, no one here will
slumber
Yeah, let's howl again, no one here will sleep

Pusscat Grimes, Boddington and Lumley paused for breath. Toothless Tom snored loudly. He was fast asleep.